To Matthew—

I hope you enjoy reading these poems at home.

Jn McLaughl

Judy

Poems on Fruits
& Odes to Veggies

Where Healthy Eating
Starts With a Poem

Judith Natelli McLaughlin

For the biggest champion of my endeavors
Mom

For the infuser of poetry into my life
Dad

For the one who makes me laugh the hardest,
my greatest supporter
Brian

&
For the three girls who are my dreams come true
Katie, Lindsay and Maggie

First Edition

Copyright © 2008 by Judith Natelli McLaughlin
Millburn, New Jersey 07041

Library of Congress Control Number: 2008907161

ISBN: 978-0-615-23837-1

Listen

Listen to me talking, child
Hear me when I say
Eat your fruits and veggies, child
Five or more a day

A symphony of colors, child
Tastes both tart and sweet
Sizes LARGE or tiny, child
Try them all to eat

Ding Dong

Ding dong goes the ring of my cell phone
I answer and then start to talk,
"Let's go to the movies on Monday
At the corner we'll meet and then walk."

The answer I got was pure silence
I thought that my friend was quite rude.
"If you don't want to go to the movies
Just tell me you're not in the mood."

I thought I was talking to Hannah
Oh what a hysterical hoot
By mistake I picked up a banana
It seems I was talking to fruit.

Bananas are totally tasty
But I'm left with a problem you see
I still want to go to the movies
Will you go to the movies with me?

(I'll bring the bananas.)

Tomatoes

Grape tomatoes
Vine tomatoes
Steak tomatoes too

Red tomatoes
Green tomatoes
I know what to do

Dice them, slice them
Mince them, seed them
Put them on a plate

Eat them,
feed them
To yourself…

They taste
really great!

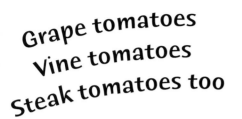

Cantaloupe

"Cantaloupe today?" Asked the handsome Mr. Harry.

"Can't elope today," I said. "I'm way too young to marry."

Zucchini

Zucchini is a lovely word
It rolls right off your tongue
Zucchini is a melody
A word that should be sung
Bellowed **LOUD** or whispered soft
Say it either way
It's almost operatic
In a veggie sort of way
Sing out loud and you'll agree
There is no squash to beat it
But after all the singing
Kindly slice it up and eat it!

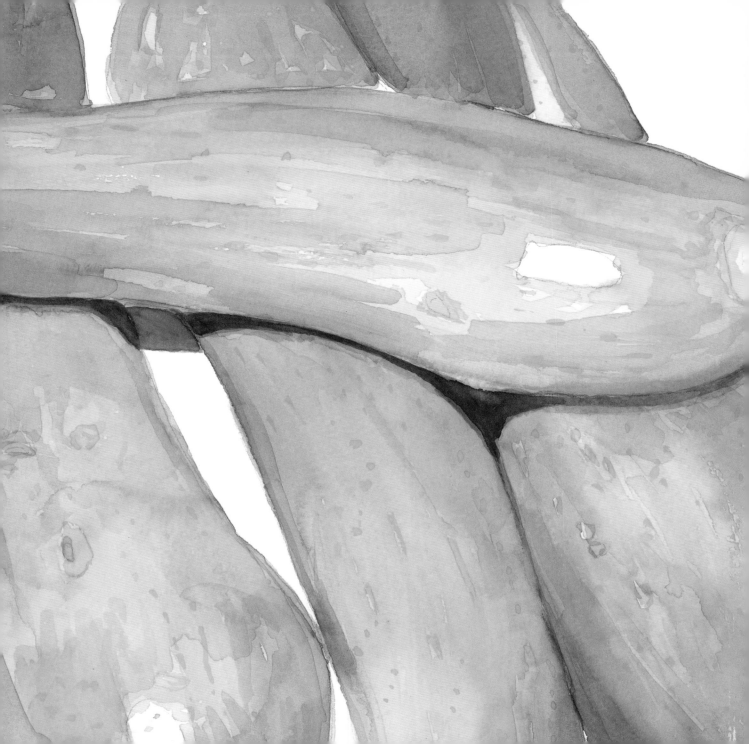

Apples

If an apple a day keeps the doctor away
Is it true eating two will help ward off the flu?
Do you think eating three prevents stings from a bee?
Dare I say eat up four and your warts are no more?
Eating five, so I hear, cleans out wax from your ear
And devouring six prevents lice, flees and tics
Eating seven's the way to make zits go away
Consume eight if you're prone to the break of a bone
Ingest nine if you wish to stop smelling like fish
I could spew 'til I'm blue apple fiction for you

But instead I'll just eat
this Delicious, red treat

Artichokes

Artie chokes on chocolate chowder
Artichokes on rice

Artie chokes on pumpkin pie
Laced with pepper spice

Artichokes on fettuccine
Barley, beans and peas

Lasagna, parmesan
And on Pecorino cheese

Artie chokes on chile
Simmered with a hockey puck

Artichokes on Caesar salad,
Sushi, roasted duck

Artie chokes or artichokes
Confusing, it is true

But if you do not try this food?
The arti JOKE'S on you!

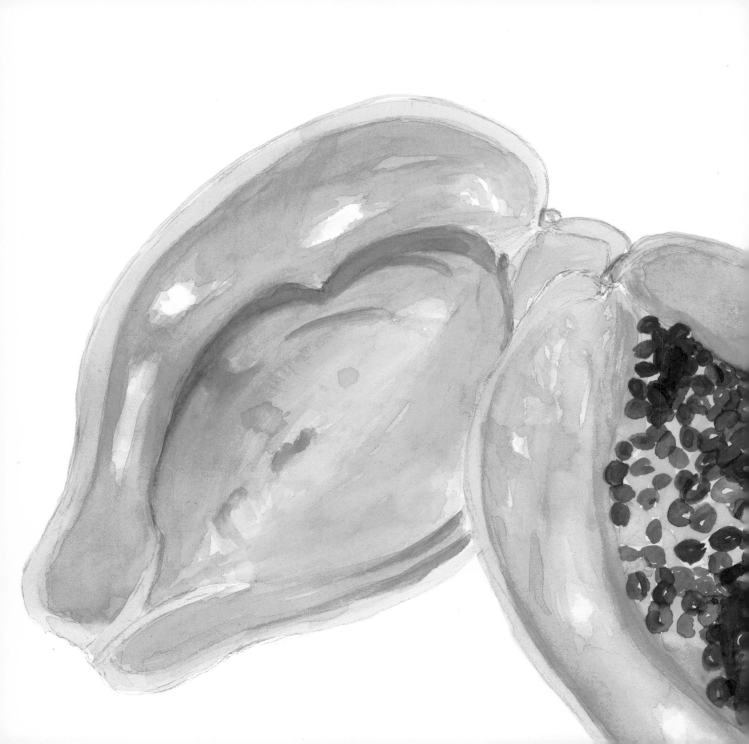

Papaya

Oh me-a and oh my-a
How I love to eat papaya
More than candy, apple pie, a
Hefty heap of jambalaya,
Toasted piece of marble rye, a
Salted, golden, crunchy fry, a
Sundae piled to the sky, a
Question often asked is why, a
Kid like me should love papaya?
Single bite'll tell you why, a
Tangy taste that's sweet not dry, a
Juicy nectar drips down by, a
Waiting mouth to gratify, a
Piece of yellow-gold papaya
Is the thing to satisfy, a
Boy like me named Jeremiah

Asparagus

Asparagus spears
Make asparagus pie,
Or asparagus quiche,
Or asparagus soup, or
Risotto. I don't know
A thing you can't do
With asparagus spears
Even put them in stew.

Pan roasted asparagus
perfect to please
Frittata? De nada —
Just add eggs and cheese.

Asparagus spears
Make asparagus salad,
Asparagus flan,
Or asparagus fry.
Packaged like pencils
In red, green or white
Put asparagus spears
On your menu tonight.

Watermelon

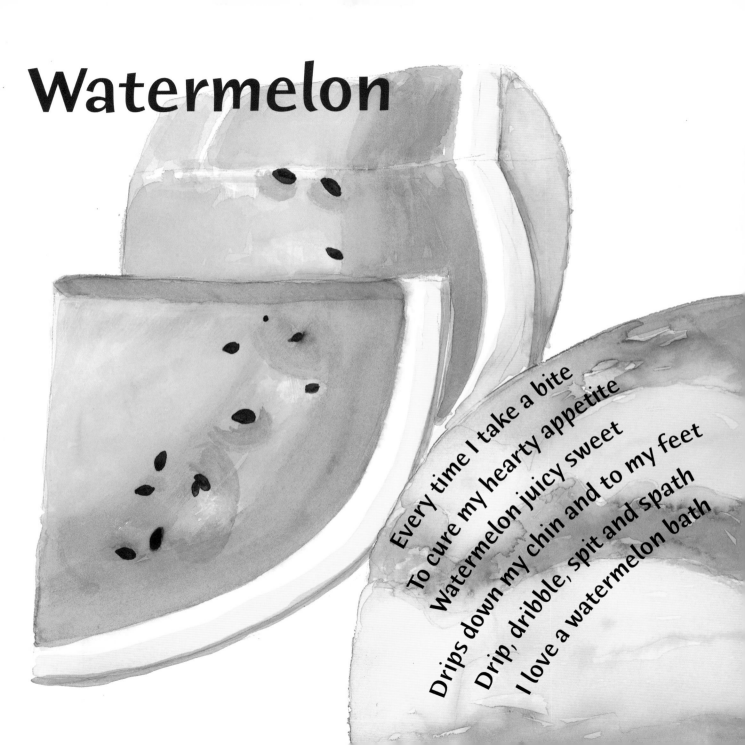

Every time I take a bite
To cure my hearty appetite
Watermelon juicy sweet
Drips down my chin and to my feet
Drip, dribble, spit and spath
I love a watermelon bath

Ping pong perfect peppers,
Pickled perfect peppers please
Pit pat pulpy peppers,
Planting peppers pretty please?

Pepper pizza plated pink,
Pretty prancing pepper pie
Picky people picking peppers,
Plucking peppers pull pat pry

Peppers

Peaches

Peachy, peachy, peachy keen, I'm feeling fine today. I'm looking pretty as a peach in each and every way. My pleated pants are colored peach. My blouse is peach as well. My peach belt and shoes both cover me, my peach purse holds what you love, 'cause when it's really what you love. A peach. My scent a peachy smell. My painted toes are polished peach. My scent a peach, there's nothing else.

Eggplant

Crack an egg, mix it up
Shells and yolk and all

Dig a hole in the ground
Just as wide as tall

Pour the egg in the hole
Using love and care

Cover it up with dirt
Water, sit and stare

See a leaf sprout right up
Don't say that you can't

Now you ask, what it is?
Naturally, eggplant

If you don't believe me
Then go ask your mother
If you do believe me
I'll tell you another

Poppagrape

Poppagrape is not a fad
Poppagrape is not a dad
Poppagrape is what you do

With juicy red
And green grapes too!

Acorn
Squash

The squirrel's a brave and brazen sort
Who flies from tree to tree for sport

He hunts for acorns high and low
And saves them up for winter's snow

When trees are bare, acorns no more
The squirrel comes up to my front door

As if to ask for food from me
"I took no acorns from your tree!"

For acorn's not my favorite nosh
Unless it's buttered acorn squash

Berries

Berries boysen, berries currant
Berries rasp and berries straw
Berries black and berries huckle
How I love my berries raw

I love berries, every kind
But berries blue are best to eat
Tell me now which berry's best
For you to have a tasty treat?

Carrots

Carrots orange, long and bright
Make my snowman's nose tonight

Carrots shredded thin and fair
Make lovely, layered orange hair

Carrots crunchy, cold and sweet
Make my favorite snack to eat

Oranges

The color orange brings to mind
A plethora of things quite kind
The setting sun just as it dips
An orange pop pressed to my lips

A plastic pail and shovel set
A basketball shot through a net
Everything that's Halloween
And all the pumpkins I have seen

Of all the orange things I know
The one for me that steals the show
Is the fruit whose color's same
As setting suns, a fruit whose name

Is called this color, vibrant, bright
A fragrant, odorous delight
A fruit with quite a heavy rind
But peel it back and you will find

Sections tender, juicy sweet
A snack that's quite a tasty treat
What is this fruit? Just take a guess
If you say orange, I say yes

Parsnips

Despite the similarity
And vague familiarity
The startling reality
A carrot this is not

Its look is bland and creamier
Its nutty taste extremier
Some large and quite supremier
This root, it hits the spot

So now I have you wondering
And clamoring and blundering
"What vegetable?" You're thundering
A parsnip we have got

Eat parsnips all parsnipitty
In stews you'll shout out, "yippity!"
A flavor deep and dripitty
Put parsnips in your pot

Lettuce

Let us in the house
I'll stay.

Let us in the game
I'll play.

Let us in the show
I'll sing.

Let us in the park
I'll swing.

Let us in the zoo
I'll treat.

Lettuce in the bowl
I'll eat.

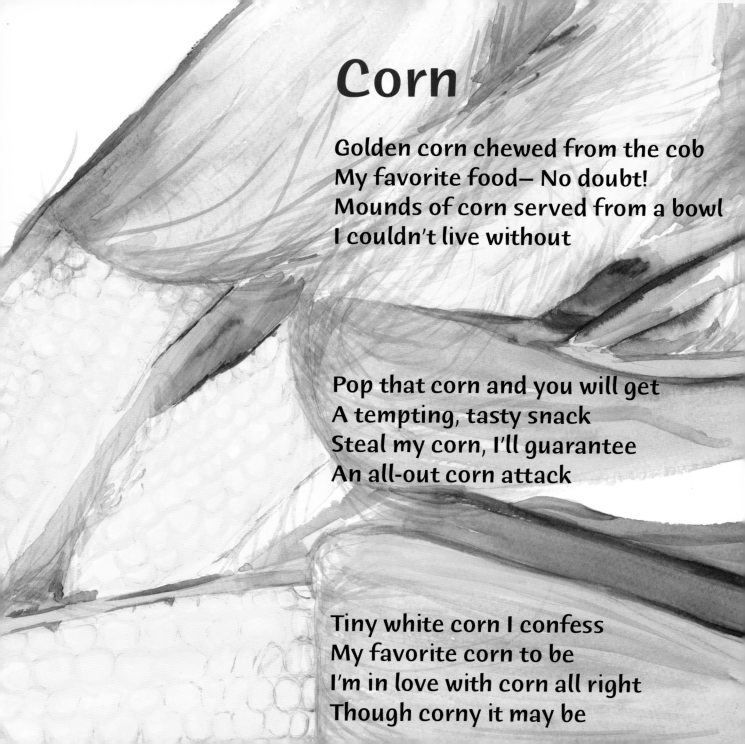

Corn

Golden corn chewed from the cob
My favorite food— No doubt!
Mounds of corn served from a bowl
I couldn't live without

Pop that corn and you will get
A tempting, tasty snack
Steal my corn, I'll guarantee
An all-out corn attack

Tiny white corn I confess
My favorite corn to be
I'm in love with corn all right
Though corny it may be